The Ideal
Home Music Library

Compiled and Edited by Albert E. Wier

Volume VI

Selected Dance Music

. . .

Piano Solo

New York: - Charles Scribner's Sons

Copyright 1913 by Charles Scribner's Sons

THE IDEAL HOME MUSIC LIBRARY

VOLUME VI—SELECTED DANCE MUSIC

TABLE OF CONTENTS—TITLES

THE IDEAL HOME MUSIC LIBRARY

VOLUME VI—SELECTED DANCE MUSIC

TABLE OF CONTENTS—DANCES

March Of The Little Pierrots.

A. BOSC.

Allegro vivo.

Piano.

con Ped.

Trio.

D.C. al Fine.

My Treasure

Waltzes

E. Becucci

8

3.

p con Ped.

P scherzando

cresc.

ff con fuoco

ff

p

1.   2.

p

Gold And Silver

Waltzes

F. Lehar

14

Under The Double Eagle
March

J. F. Wagner

Roses From The South

Waltzes

J. Strauss

Monte Cristo
Hungarian - Waltz

I. Kotlar

Piu lento.

Piu lento.

lento.

Presto.

Gondolier

Waltzes

O. Roeder

Exhibition
Two-Step

Philipp Fahrbach

Trio.

D.C. al Fine.

The Skaters
Waltzes

Tempo di Valse

E. Waldteufel

The Roses

Waltzes

Olivier Metra

3.

Valse Bleue

Alfred Margis

TRIO

ben cantando

Tempo I

Lorraine
Two-Step

Louis Ganne

Trio.

p dolce e molto cantabile.

On The Beautiful Blue Danube

Waltzes

Johann Strauss

D. C. ad lib al 𝄐

La Serenata
Italian Waltzes

D'Arcy Jaxone

ing   light.   The night! Good night! Good night! _____   And

dream   of __ me   till   morn - ing   light.   f

2.

Fine.

D.S. al Fine.

dolce cantabile.

3.

Sourire d'Avril

(April-Smile.)

WALTZES

Maurice Depret

La Sorella
Two-Step

Ch. Borel-Clerc

Tempo di Marcia.

con Ped. ad lib.

Trio.

Coda.

Estudiantina.
Waltzes.

Emile Waldteufel.

3.

Myosotis

Waltzes

C. Lowthian

Tempo di Valse

1.

dolce ma marc.

con Ped.

Over The Waves

Waltzes

Valse

Legato

J. Rosas

'A Frangesa!

Two-Step

P. Mario Costa

Trio.

The Sirens

Waltzes

Emile Waldteufel

Ciribiribin

Waltz

A.Pestalozza

Flirtation
Waltzes

P. A. Steck.

The Standard-Bearer

March

Philipp Fahrbach

Fine

D.S. al Fine.

Artist Life

Waltzes

J. Strauss

In Old Madrid

Waltzes

J. Meissler

D.C. al Fine.

3.

D. C. al Fine

Vienna Beauties

Waltzes

C. M. Ziehrer

Entry Of The Gladiators
March

Julius Fucîk

Grandioso.

The Merry Widow

Waltzes

F. Lehar

Slow Waltz Tempo
Con molto espressione.

Con Ped.

1. *pp*

Waves Of The Danube
Waltzes

J. Ivanovici

2.

4.

mf

1. 2. *Last.* *Fine.*

f *tr* *tr*

tr *tr* 1. 2. *ff* *p*

D.S. al Fine.

The Dudes
March

J. F. Wagner

Sympathie

Waltzes

E. Mezzacapo

D.C. al Fine.

D.C. ad lib. al Fine.

Love's Dreamland

Waltzes

Otto Roeder

D. C. al Fine.

2.

136

VOL. VI- 136

D.C. ad lib.

Santiago
Spanish Waltzes

A. Corbin

D.C. ad lib.

Apache Dance
Valse Lente

Arr. by A. Hewitt.

Mazurka ben marcato

Valse Vivo.

Valse.

My Dream
Waltzes

E. Waldteufel

D.C. al 3

The Doll

Waltzes

J. Bayer

D.C. al Fine.

Fine. *mf*

mf

D.S. al Fine.

Jolly Fellows
Waltzes

R. Vollstedt

Under the Banner of Victory.
March.

F. von Blon.

Trio.

A Waltz Dream
Waltzes

Oscar Straus

The First Kiss

Waltzes

Tempo di Valse

Georges Lamothe

D.C. Valse al Fine.

Hoch Hapsburg
March

J. N. Kral

176

Tre - Jolie
Waltzes

E. Waldteufel

Waltz D.C. ad lib.

Cornflower
Waltzes

C. Coote Jr

Valse Moderato

3.

La Gitana

Waltzes

E. Bucalossi

Petite Tonkinoise
Schottische

V. Scotto

Tempo di Schottische

The Skirt Dance
Schottische

From "FAUST UP TO DATE."

Meyer Lutz

1st time **p** 2nd time **f**

1st time p 2nd time ff

Dixie Days

Cakewalk.

A. Hewitt.

Trio.

Campus Echoes
Quadrille

A. Hewitt

Alma Mater O

2.

1st & 3rd time. 2nd & 4th time. (Jingle Bells) 1st & 3rd time.

(Old Black Joe) 2nd & 4th time

D.C.

204

(Where Has My Little Dog Gone)

Coda

My Last Cigar

(I Was Seeing Nellie Home)
March 1st & 3rd time

1st & 3rd time   2nd & 4th time

John Brown's Body
March 2nd & 4th time

Opera Strains
Lanciers

A. Hewitt

Copyright 1913 by Charles Scribner's Sons.

(Erminie)

(Chimes of Normandy.)

(Boccaccio) 2nd & 4th time

(Merry Widows)

(Erminie)

(Faust)
March 1st & 3rd times

March 2nd & 4th times

A Country Weddin'
Barn Dance

A. Hewitt

Tempo di Schottische

Trio.

Kutschke-Polka

Ludwig Stasny

Tempo di Polka

Trio.

D.C. al ⊕ Coda.

Coda.

One Heart, One Mind

Polka-Mazurka

Johann Strauss

Introduction

Tempo di Mazurka

Trio.

D.C. ad lib.

The Gipsy
Mazurka

Louis Ganne

The Hornpipe Polka

Frank J. Smith

L'Esprit Français
Polka.

E. Waldteufel

Pizzicato - Polka

Johann and Josef Strauss.

Più Allegro.

Coda.

D.C. ⊕ to Coda.

The First Love
Redowa

A. Wallerstein

Molto dolce e moderato

Trio.

First Heart Throbs

Gavotte

R. Eilenberg

Trio.

D.C.ad lib.

Qui Vive

Galop

Wilhelm Ganz

Vivo leggiero

Trio.

Coda.

Jolly Brothers

Galop

F. Budik

To Trio.　Fine.

Trio.

D.C. al Fine.

In Old Madrid

(Bolero)

H. Trotere

Don Juan

Minuet

W. A. Mozart

Olga

Varsovienne

F. Beyer

Military Polonaise

F. Chopin

Allegro con brio

con Ped.

Arkansas Traveller

Jig

The Campbells Are Comin'

Chorus Jig

con Ped.

College Hornpipe
(Sailor's Hornpipe)

con Ped.

The Devil's Dream
Hornpipe

Fisher's Hornpipe

Highland Fling

The Irish Washerwoman
Reel

Life Is All Checkered

Jig

Jig

Miss Mc Leod's Reel

Old Kent Road

Jig

Old Zip Coon
Jig

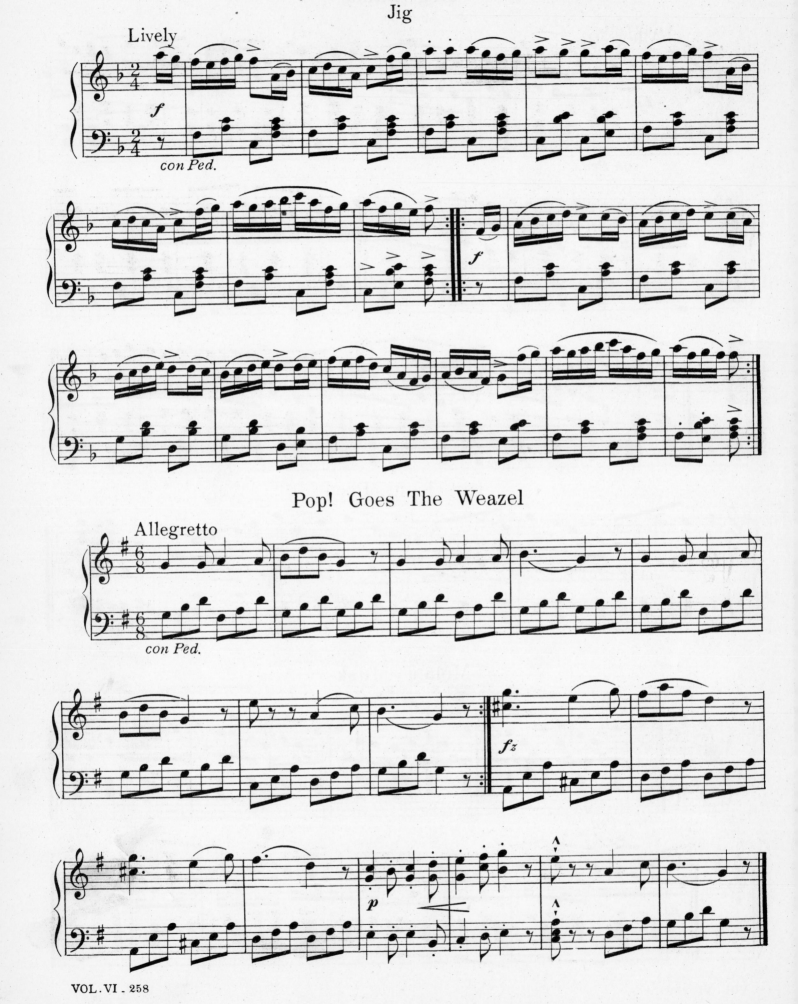

Pop! Goes The Weazel

Clog Dance

Money Musk

Rory O' More
Jig

Soldier's Joy
Hornpipe

St. Patrick's Day
Jig

The White Cockade
Reel

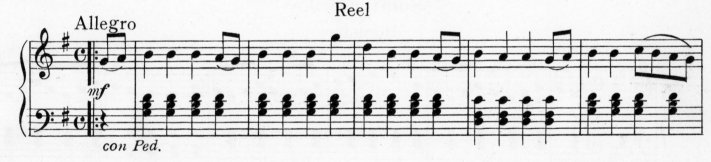

United States
Two-Step

England
(Sir Roger de Coverly)

Scotland
(Strathspey)

Ireland
(Jig)

Germany
(Waltz)

France
(Gavotte)

Poland
(Mazurka)

Bohemia
(Krakoviak)

Fine.

D.C. al Fine

Hungary
(Czardas)

Allegretto

con Ped.

Russia
(Cossack Dance)

Denmark
(Peasant Dance)

Sweden

Allegro non troppo

Norway
Reel

Allegro

Spain
(La Cachucha)

Allegro moderato

Italy
(Peasant Dance)

Allegro

con Ped.

Switzerland

(Oberländer)